Who Has a Bill?

by Judy Nayer
Illustrated by Maxie Chambliss

SCHOLASTIC

Who has a bill?

A  has a bill.
bird

The  will sip with it.
bird

Who has a bill?

A  has a bill.

bird

The  will tap with it.

bird

3

Who has a bill?

A  has a bill.

bird

It has a in it.

bug

Who has a bill?

A  has a bill.

bird

It bit a  with it.

nut

Who has a bill?

A  has a bill.

bird

The will fill it up with .

bird

fish

Who has a bill?

A  has a bill.

bird

It has a very big bill!

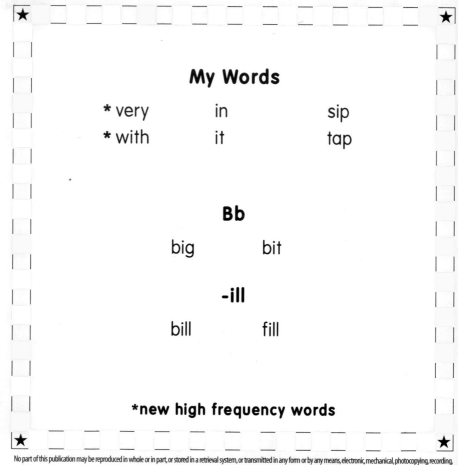

My Words

* very	in	sip
* with	it	tap

Bb

big   bit

-ill

bill   fill

*new high frequency words